THE CITY OF EMBER

by
Jeanne DuPrau

Student Packet

Written by
Angela Frith Antrim

Contains masters for:

	2 Prereading Activities
	10 Vocabulary Activities
	1 Study Guide
	2 Character Analysis Activities
	1 Comprehension Activity
	1 Literary Analysis Activity
	3 Quizzes
	1 Novel Test
PLUS	Detailed Answer Key
	and Scoring Rubric

Note

The 2004 Yearling paperback edition of the novel, © 2003 by Jeanne DuPrau, was used to prepare this guide. The page references may differ in other editions. Novel ISBN: 0-375-82274-7

Please note: Parts of this novel deal with sensitive, mature issues. Please assess the appropriateness of this book for the age level and maturity of your students prior to reading and discussing it with them.

ISBN: 978-1-56137-066-5

To order, contact your local school supply store, or—
Novel Units, Inc.
P.O. Box 97
Bulverde, TX 78163-0097

Web site: www.novelunits.com

Name _____

Clue Search

Directions: Collect information about the book for each of the items. Write down the information, and then make some predictions about the book.

Information Source	Information Provided
Dedication	
Title	
Cover Illustration	
Teasers on the cover	
Friends' recommendations	
Reviewers' recommendations/awards won	

Your predictions about the book:

Be a Detective!

Directions: Check out the book by looking at the cover and thumbing through the pages. Then, ask yourself who, what, where, when, why, and how. Write your questions in the spaces below. Exchange papers with a partner, and answer each other's questions.

Who?

_____
_____
_____
_____

What?

_____
_____
_____
_____

Where?

_____
_____
_____
_____

When?

_____
_____
_____

Why?

_____
_____
_____
_____
_____

How?

_____
_____
_____
_____
_____

Vocabulary Chart

weary	endeavor	anxious	frayed
labyrinth	prosper	generator	trudge
immensely	threadbare	reverberating	resonant
kiosks	serene	antics	

Directions: Write each vocabulary word in the correct place on the chart below.

Noun	Verb	Adjective	Adverb

Name _____

Vocabulary Chart

anticipation	clamor	throng	chasm
complicated	puzzled	plodding	absolute
gauges	infected		

Directions: Write each vocabulary word in the left-hand column of the chart. Complete the chart by placing a check mark in the column that best describes your familiarity with each word. Working with a partner, find and read the line where each word appears in the story. Find the meaning of each word in the dictionary. Together with your partner, choose ten of the words checked in the last column. On a separate sheet of paper, use each of those words in a sentence.

Vocabulary Word	I Can Define	I Have Seen/Heard	New Word For Me

Name _____

The City of Ember
Activity #5 • Vocabulary
Chapters 5–6

muddled	wistfully	threaded	spectacle
whimper	tottered	defiant	summon
incoherently	murmur	glinted	incomprehensible
wrenched	chortled		

Vocabulary Board

Finish

Give a synonym. | Free space. | Use the word in a sentence with *therefore* in it. | Give an example of the word. | Use as the third word in a sentence. | Go back 2 spaces.

Free space. | If your word is a noun, go to Finish. | Define. | Attach an emotion to the word; explain. | If your word is a verb, cheer and go ahead 5 spaces.

You're in the dog house; go back 10 spaces. | Use the word in a simile. | Define. | Dramatize the word. | Define. | Leap ahead 2 spaces.

Give a synonym. | Put the word into an alliterative phrase. | Go back 3 spaces. | Tell the word's origin. | Find a word starting with the last letter.

Tell the part of speech. | Define. | Give an antonym. | Use in a sentence. | Give a synonym.

Start

All rights reserved

© Novel Units, Inc. 7

Vocabulary Match

Directions: Match each vocabulary word to its correct definition.

1. _____ pried
2. _____ extract
3. _____ tattered
4. _____ jumble
5. _____ frantic
6. _____ severe
7. _____ eagerly
8. _____ illegible
9. _____ reluctantly
10. _____ recoiling
11. _____ enraged
12. _____ crevices
13. _____ significance

a. anxiously, impatiently

b. extremely angry or upset

c. meaning, importance

d. nervous, frenzied

e. forced open

f. torn, ragged

g. disorganized pile, mess

h. narrow cracks or openings

i. serious, critical

j. to pull out or remove

k. shrinking back in fear or disgust

l. impossible or difficult to read

m. hesitantly, with suspicion or caution

Vocabulary Card Game

Teacher Directions:

- Photocopy and cut out the following pages.
- Give one card to each student in the class.
- The student who has the starred card begins by reading his/her question.
- The student who has the card with the correct vocabulary word responds and then reads his/her question.
- Play continues in this manner until all cards have been read.

 self-conscious

Who has a word that means a
mechanical device?

mechanism

Who has a word that means alarmed
or suddenly surprised?

startled

Who has a word that means
shuffling or hurrying?

scuffling

Who has a word that means
low and harsh?

gruff

Who has a word that means filled with
overwhelming amazement or wonder?

astonished

Who has a word that means walked
slowly or strolled?

Name _____

---

ambled

- -

Who has a word that means sneaking or waiting undetected?

---

lurking

- -

Who has a word that means raspy?

---

hoarse

- -

Who has a word that means unclearly or blurrily?

---

blearily

- -

Who has a word that means amazing things or wonders?

---

marvels

- -

Who has a word that means carefully and deliberately?

---

methodically

- -

Who has a word that means drew back or tensed?

---

winced

- -

Who has a word that means embarrassed or excessively aware of how one appears to others?

Vocabulary Wheel

sternly	gloomier	distracted	astonishment
tainted	sauntering	delectable	beckoned
fiercely	shrill	slogans	

Directions: Write each vocabulary word on a piece of paper (one word per piece). Make a spinner using the circle below. Now play the following game with a classmate. (It is a good idea to have a dictionary and thesaurus handy.) Place the papers in a small container. The first player draws a word from the container. The player then spins the spinner and follows the direction where the pointer lands. For example, if the player draws the word "shrill" and lands on "Define," the player must define the word shrill. If the player's partner accepts the answer as correct, the first player scores one point and play passes to the second player. If the player's partner challenges the answer, the first player uses a dictionary or thesaurus to prove the answer is correct. If the player can prove the answer is correct, the player earns two points. If the player cannot prove the answer is correct, the opposing player earns two points. Play continues until all the words have been used. The player with the most points wins.

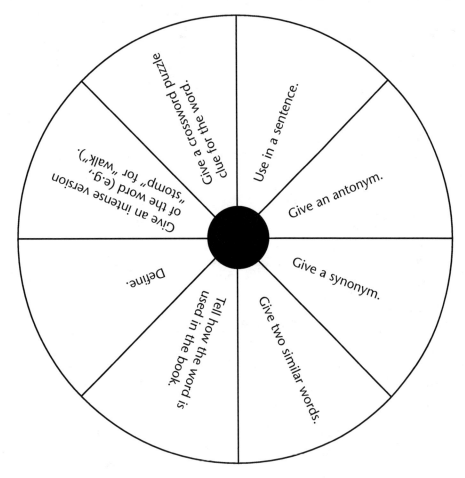

Name _____

Vocabulary Sentence Sets

deciphering	rickety	egress	emerged
urgently	splendid	clarity	realm
plunder	gorging	bewilderment	seize
spurting	surging	threshold	consulted

Directions: Choose 15 vocabulary words from the list above. Write the words on the numbered lines below.

1. _____   2. _____

3. _____   4. _____

5. _____   6. _____

7. _____   8. _____

9. _____   10. _____

11. _____   12. _____

13. _____   14. _____

15. _____

On a separate sheet of paper, use each of the following sets of words in an original sentence. Your sentences should show that you know the meanings of the vocabulary words as they are used in the story.

Sentence 1: words 8 and 4
Sentence 2: words 9 and 3
Sentence 3: words 1 and 10
Sentence 4: words 11 and 7
Sentence 5: words 15 and 13
Sentence 6: words 3 and 6
Sentence 7: words 12 and 4
Sentence 8: words 14 and 9
Sentence 9: words 5 and 2
Sentence 10: words 7 and 6

Name _____

Crossword Puzzle

desperate	merchandise	generations	feeble
burly	curtly	civic	impudence
accomplice	abundance	majesty	tumult

Directions: Select ten vocabulary words from above. Create a crossword puzzle answer key by filling in the grid below. Be sure to number the squares for each word. Blacken any spaces not used by the letters. Then, write clues to the crossword puzzle. Number the clues to match the numbers in the squares. The teacher will give each student a blank grid. Make a blank copy of your crossword puzzle for other students to answer. Exchange your clues with someone else, and solve the blank puzzle s/he gives you. Check the completed puzzles with the answer keys.

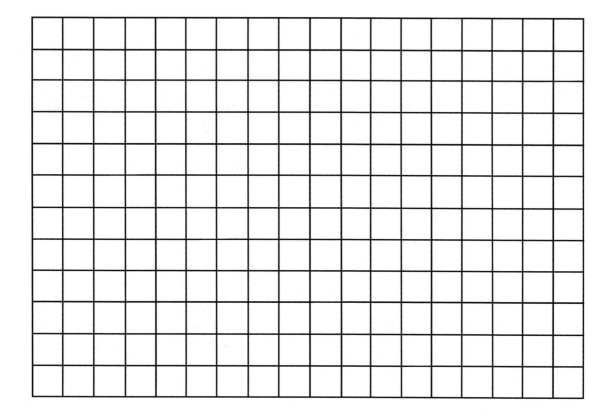

Name _____

dread	harmonies	dispersing	queasy
hoisted	rungs	hostile	tether
churning	plunged	shrieking	gleefully

Directions: Each of the words below is either a synonym or an antonym of a vocabulary word. Write the correct vocabulary word on the line beside each question. Circle letter S or A to identify whether each word is a synonym or antonym.

1. whispering   _____   S   A

2. friendly   _____   S   A

3. steps   _____   S   A

4. raised   _____   S   A

5. courage   _____   S   A

6. swirling   _____   S   A

7. gathering   _____   S   A

8. melodies   _____   S   A

9. sick   _____   S   A

10. rope   _____   S   A

11. leaped   _____   S   A

12. sadly   _____   S   A

Name _____

Word Map

refugees	relentlessly	infinitely	vast
billowed	crimson	seeped	trill
catastrophes	pondered	gullies	

Directions: Complete a word map for at least five of the vocabulary words listed above.

Synonyms	Magazine cut-out, drawing, or symbol that shows what the word means
_____	
_____	
_____	
_____	
_____	
_____	

Word

_____

Definition in your own words	Word used in a sentence
_____	_____
_____	_____
_____	_____
_____	_____

Name _____

Directions: Answer the following questions on a separate sheet of paper. Use the questions to guide your reading and prepare for class discussions.

The Instructions–Chapter 2

1. How long have people lived in Ember?
2. What happened to the Instructions?
3. At what age do people begin working in Ember?
4. How do people get supplies in Ember?
5. Explain why electricity is so important to Ember's citizens.
6. How does Doon anger the mayor on Assignment Day?
7. Why are messengers important in Ember?
8. Why is Ember's light bulb supply so important to the people?
9. Describe the supplies and luxuries available in Ember.
10. Who was the seventh mayor of Ember?

Chapters 3–4

1. Why does it surprise Doon to see a river in the Pipeworks?
2. Will Doon be allowed to work on the generator? Why or why not?
3. How far underground is the Pipeworks?
4. In what condition is the Pipeworks? How does this compare to the rest of Ember?
5. Why does Doon believe that he can fix the generator?
6. What advice does Doon's father give him about working in the Pipeworks?
7. Besides Clary, who does Lina see at the greenhouses?
8. Are Ember's citizens allowed to express their concerns or disapproval of the mayor's decisions?

Chapters 5–6

1. What does Lina usually eat for breakfast? Why do you think she usually eats the same thing?

2. Is Lina's job the main source of her family's income? How do you know?

3. Who is Looper?

4. How does Lina feel when she loses Poppy during the blackout?

5. How long is the blackout? Why is it significant that Ember's citizens monitor the exact length of each blackout?

6. Why does Mayor Cole call a town meeting?

7. What is Granny doing when Lina returns home?

Chapters 7–8

1. What about the note sparks Lina's curiosity?

2. Why does Lina ask Captain Fleery to look at the Instructions?

3. What does Captain Fleery hypothesize about the Instructions?

4. What do Ember's citizens believe about the rest of the world?

5. Contrast Ember's current storerooms to the storerooms of Granny's childhood.

6. To whom does Lina write a note about the Instructions?

7. Which of Doon's qualities does Lina think will help him to decode the Instructions?

8. List three things that Doon has discovered since he began working in the Pipeworks.

9. How are books organized in Ember's library?

Chapters 9–10

1. Who is Mrs. Murdo?

2. What do Doon and Lina each like to draw?

3. What is the odd mechanism on the box that holds the Instructions?

4. Why does it surprise Doon to learn that Lina wants to go into the Pipeworks?

5. What do Doon and Lina see during their exploration in the Pipeworks?

6. Why does Dr. Tower think she may not be able to help Granny?

7. What is Granny worried about finding?

8. Why is Lina unable to tell what time it is at night?

Chapters 11–12

1. What is the Singing?
2. Where do Lina and Poppy live after Granny dies?
3. Why does Lina believe that she matures after Granny dies?
4. Why doesn't Lizzie stop when Lina calls to her on the street?
5. Who is Lizzie's boyfriend?
6. Why do most people in Ember decide to stay home?
7. To where does the door in the Pipeworks lead?
8. Who gives stolen food and supplies to the mayor?
9. Whom do Lina and Doon tell about the mayor's secret room full of food and supplies?

Chapters 13–14

1. Whom does Lina consult for advice about the Instructions?
2. How does Mayor Cole demonstrate that he is foolish and wicked?
3. What is growing in Lina's room?
4. Who figures out the Instructions' title? What is the complete title, and what does it mean?
5. How does Doon get a key to the Pipeworks?
6. Why has no one discovered the ladder along the wall in the Pipeworks?
7. What is unusual about the door Lina tries to open?
8. How do Lina and Doon create movable light? Why is movable light useful and important?
9. Why haven't Doon and Lina ever seen a boat?

Name _____

Chapters 15–16

1. Why is there only one boat in the first room Lina and Doon discover?
2. Why does Doon take the candle and matches with him?
3. List three items that Doon packs to take with him when he leaves Ember.
4. How does Nammy Proggs help Doon?
5. What about leaving Ember concerns Lina most?
6. To whom is Lina delivering a note when the guards arrest her?
7. What happens at the Singing?
8. How does Lina escape Mayor Cole and the "Prison Room"?
9. What does Lina see in the darkness?

Chapters 17–18

1. What does Doon leave for his father?
2. What does Doon have that no citizen of Ember has ever had before?
3. Whom does Lina bring with her to the Pipeworks?
4. What is the most terrible part of the boat ride for Lina and Doon?
5. Why can't Doon, Lina, and Poppy return to Ember?
6. What does Poppy find along the path at the end of the river?
7. What does Lina forget to do before she meets Doon at the Pipeworks?

Chapters 19–20

1. Where is Ember located?
2. List five things that Doon and Lina see for the first time after they emerge from the tunnel.
3. Who left the diary in the tunnel?
4. What animal do Doon and Lina see in the meadow? Are there animals, other than insects, in Ember?
5. What do Doon and Lina see at the bottom of the chasm?
6. Who finds the note?

Name _____

Character Analysis Blocks

Directions: Use the blocks below to describe Doon Harrow.

Who is the character?

What does the character do?	Why does he do it?

What, if anything, is significant about the character's name?	What is the nature of this character's actions? (reactive, active, important, consequential, secondary)	What is the significance of the book's time and place to the character?

What is unusual or important about the character?	How does the character change in the story?	Does the character remind you of another character from another book? Who?	Do you know anyone similar to this character?

© Novel Units, Inc.

Venn Diagram

Directions: Use the Venn diagram to compare and contrast Lina Mayfleet and Doon Harrow.

Lina   Doon

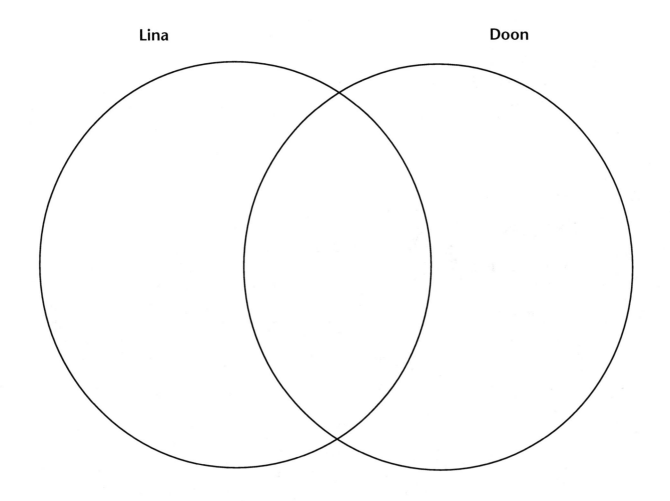

Name _____

Story Map

Directions: Use information from the novel to complete the story map below.

Characters _____

_____

Setting

Time and Place _____

_____

Problem

Problem _____

_____

_____

Goal

Goal _____

_____

_____

Beginning ⟶ Development ⟶ Outcome

Episodes

_____

_____

_____

_____

Resolution _____

Resolution

_____

_____

_____

Name _____

Solving Problems

Directions: List six problems the characters in the novel face. Then complete the rest of the chart. For each problem, circle which solution you think is best—yours or the character's.

Problem	Character's Solution	Your Solution

Name _____

A. True/False

____ 1. Ember is approximately 241 years old.

____ 2. Ember's children graduate from school when they are 12 years old.

____ 3. On Assignment Day, Doon draws "Pipeworks laborer."

____ 4. Ember is powered by a deteriorating generator.

____ 5. Doon and Lizzie used to be friends when they were younger.

____ 6. Lina lives with her parents and grandmother.

____ 7. Lina believes another city exists outside of Ember.

____ 8. A river runs through the Pipeworks.

____ 9. Lina finds the Instructions in a closet at Mrs. Murdo's home.

____ 10. People in Ember have never seen fire.

B. Identification: Match each character with the correct description.

11. ___ Lina	a. sells colored pencils
12. ___ Poppy	b. runs Ember's greenhouses
13. ___ Looper	c. works as a Supply Depot clerk
14. ___ Doon	d. Assistant Guard to the mayor
15. ___ Mayor Morethwart	e. Lina's baby sister
16. ___ Clary	f. current mayor of Ember
17. ___ Lizzie	g. oversees all of Ember's messengers
18. ___ Captain Fleery	h. works as a messenger
19. ___ Barton Snode	i. former mayor of Ember
20. ___ Mayor Cole	j. works in the Pipeworks

Name _____

A. Quotations: Match each quotation to the correct character from the novel. Note: Some characters may be used more than once.

_____ 1. "Actually, I *saw* a door where I didn't expect to see one—out in Tunnel 351."

_____ 2. "What's best for you is to sleep today. Your good granddaughter will take care of you."

_____ 3. "Did we ever find it?… The old thing my Grandfather lost…"

_____ 4. "If you add an s to this word, right where this tear in the paper is, you get 'Egress.' Do you know what that means?"

_____ 5. "He really likes me—he says my hair is the exact color of a red-hot burner on a stove."

_____ 6. "I don't want anything from Looper."

_____ 7. "I don't know. I think maybe those Instructions are just hogwash."

_____ 8. "Action will be taken, you may be sure. Some sort of action. Quite soon."

_____ 9. "Everyone has some darkness inside. It's like a hungry creature. It wants and wants and *wants* with a terrible power. And the more you give it, the bigger and hungrier it gets."

_____ 10. "Don't worry about Poppy, I'll take care of her."

a. Doon

b. Lina

c. Granny

d. Clary

e. Lizzie

f. Dr. Tower

g. Barton Snode

h. Mrs. Murdo

B. True/False

____ 11. Lina and Doon confront the mystery person outside the secret room in the Pipeworks.

____ 12. Mrs. Murdo takes in Lina and Poppy following Granny's death.

____ 13. Barton Snode is Lizzie's new boyfriend.

____ 14. Lizzie gives Lina one can of peaches and one can of creamed corn.

____ 15. Lina thinks it is unfair to hoard food instead of sharing it with others.

____ 16. The guards arrest Mayor Cole.

____ 17. The Instructions mention a rock in the Pipeworks marked with a "W" for "way out."

____ 18. Doon wants to be remembered as a hero.

____ 19. Lina and Doon attend Song Rehearsal to prepare for the Singing.

____ 20. Lina and Doon find a flashlight inside the Pipeworks' secret tunnel.

© Novel Units, Inc.

Name _____

A. Sequencing: Use the letters *a–j* to order the events below as they occur in the novel.

____ 1. Doon posts a message to his father on a public kiosk.

____ 2. Poppy finds an abandoned diary on a pathway.

____ 3. Lina tosses Clary's note down the chasm toward Ember.

____ 4. Ember experiences back-to-back blackouts.

____ 5. Lina retrieves Poppy and meets Doon at the Pipeworks' entrance.

____ 6. Mrs. Murdo picks up the bundle that has seemingly fallen from the sky.

____ 7. The mayor's guards arrest Lina.

____ 8. Lina, Doon, and Poppy witness a sunrise.

____ 9. Doon learns that he and Lina are wanted for "spreading vicious rumors."

___ 10. Lina, Doon, and Poppy travel down the river in a boat.

B. Graphic Organizer: In the circle below, write one of the novel's themes. On the surrounding spokes, identify specific scenes or issues found in the novel that relate to the theme you choose.

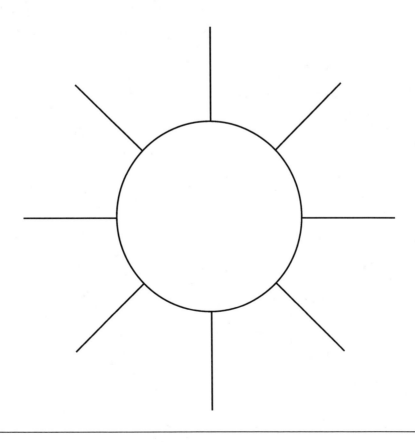

Name _____

A. Fill in the Blanks: Complete the summary below.

The novel takes place in fictional, futuristic Ember, known as "'the only

(1)_____ in the (2)_____ world,'" approximately (3)_____

years after the city's creation. The story begins on (4)_____ _____,

when all of Ember's graduating students randomly select their future careers.

(5)_____ Mayfleet longs to be a (6)_____ but instead draws a job

working in the underground (7)_____. Luckily, she trades jobs with Doon

(8)_____, who aspires to work near the city's deteriorating (9)_____.

Over time, food and supplies in Ember have become scarce, and the city now suffers from

persistent (10)_____. Lina, who struggles to take care of her (11)_____

and younger sister (12)_____, discovers scraps of paper that detail how to escape

from Ember. Unable to decode the message on her own, Lina turns to Doon for help.

Together, they follow the (13)_____ to a secret door in the Pipeworks and later

discover that (14)_____, Lizzie's (15)_____, is stealing from the city's

rations to deliver goods to (16)_____ _____. The day before the

(17)_____, Ember's only annual holiday, Lina and Doon venture to the Pipeworks

to look for a (18)_____ marked with the letter (19)_____.

A secret passageway leads them to two boxes filled with (20)_____ and

(21)_____. Using these items, they discover a (22)_____ and deduce

that the swirling (23)_____ is their source of escape from Ember. Along with Lina's

little sister, Lina and Doon journey into the (24)_____ _____.

Hours later, they come to a pathway, where (25)_____ finds an abandoned

(26)_____. Eventually, the travelers reach the earth's surface, where they witness a

(27)_____ for the first time. After discovering that Ember exists at the bottom of a

giant (28)_____, Lina tosses a (29)_____ down to the city below. The

story ends as (30)_____ _____ sees a bundle fall from the sky and

reaches forward to pick it up.

Name _____

B. **Multiple Choice:** Choose the BEST answer to each question.

____ 31. *The City of Ember* is classified as
(a) mystery
(b) nonfiction
(c) realistic fiction
(d) science fiction

____ 32. Ember is powered by
(a) a generator
(b) the sun
(c) water
(d) windmills

____ 33. Supplies in Ember
(a) are free to citizens of Ember
(b) must be carefully conserved
(c) are manufactured in large factories
(d) can be purchased at modern grocery stores

____ 34. Ember's only source(s) of light is/are
(a) candles
(b) flashlights
(c) light bulbs
(d) the sun

____ 35. People in Ember communicate via
(a) telephone
(b) written letters and notes
(c) e-mail and instant messaging programs
(d) messages delivered verbally by city messengers

____ 36. Before his death, Lina's father worked at
(a) Gathering Hall
(b) the greenhouses
(c) the Pipeworks
(d) the Supply Depot

Name _____

_____ 37. Lina visits Looper's shop to buy
     (a) colored pencils
     (b) creamed corn
     (c) light bulbs
     (d) paint

_____ 38. The Instructions are hidden in
     (a) the Pipeworks
     (b) Looper's shop
     (c) the mayor's office
     (d) a box in Granny's closet

_____ 39. Clary tells Lina that the word "egress" means
     (a) Ember
     (b) exit
     (c) express
     (d) out

_____ 40. Doon doesn't confide in his father because he
     (a) doesn't want to worry his father
     (b) doesn't get along with his father
     (c) wants his and Lina's discovery to be publicly announced
     (d) doesn't trust his father to keep his and Lina's discovery a secret

_____ 41. In a tunnel in the Pipeworks, Lina and Doon find
     (a) tools to fix the generator
     (b) food, light bulbs, and books
     (c) candles, matches, and a boat
     (d) flashlights, batteries, and a raft

_____ 42. To escape Ember, Lina and Doon must
     (a) cross the Lake of No Return
     (b) sail down the river in the Pipeworks
     (c) crawl through a secret passageway in the school
     (d) go through the mayor's secret hatch in Gathering Hall

_____ 43. Doon discovers that he and Lina are wanted for
     (a) disobeying the mayor
     (b) spreading vicious rumors
     (c) breaking into the Pipeworks
     (d) questioning Ember's management

_____ 44. Along a pathway, Poppy finds an abandoned
     (a) candle
     (b) flashlight
     (c) journal
     (d) storeroom

_____ 45. Who finds the bundle that seemingly falls from the sky?
     (a) Clary
     (b) Looper
     (c) Mayor Cole
     (d) Mrs. Murdo

C. Essay: Write a well-developed essay on one of the following topics. Use evidence and examples from the novel to support your response.

(a) How does Lina mature from the novel's beginning to its conclusion?

(b) Choose one conflict from the novel. What type of conflict is it? Which character(s) does the conflict involve? How is the conflict resolved?

(c) In Ember, children graduate from school and enter the workforce when they are 12 years old. Do you agree with this practice? Why or why not? Would you rather have a job like the children in Ember or go to school? Explain your answer.

Answer Key

Activity #1: Dedication: none; Title: *The City of Ember*; Cover Illustration: "ember" written inside a glowing light bulb; Teasers on the cover: "the first Book of Ember"; Friends' recommendations: Answers will vary; Reviewers' recommendations/awards won: ALA Notable Book, *Kirkus Reviews* Editors' Choice, New York Public Library 100 Titles for Reading and Sharing Selection; Your predictions about the book: Answers will vary.

Activity #2: Answers will vary.

Activity #3: Nouns: endeavor, labyrinth, generator, kiosks, antics; Verbs: prosper, trudge; Adjectives: weary, anxious, frayed, threadbare, reverberating, resonant, serene; Adverb: immensely

Activity #4: Answers will vary.

Activity #5: Student will play Vocabulary Board game.

Activity #6: 1. e 2. j 3. f 4. g 5. d 6. i 7. a 8. l 9. m 10. k 11. b 12. h 13. c

Activity #7: Student will play Vocabulary Card Game.

Activity #8: Student will play Vocabulary Wheel.

Activity #9: Sentence Sets will vary.

Activity #10: Crossword Puzzles will vary.

Activity #11: 1. shrieking, A 2. hostile, A 3. rungs, S 4. hoisted, S 5. dread, A 6. churning, S 7. dispersing, A 8. harmonies, S 9. queasy, S 10. tether, S 11. plunged, S 12. gleefully, A

Activity #12: Word Maps will vary.

Study Guide

The Instructions–Chapter 2: 1. approximately 241 years 2. The Instructions ended up locked inside a box in the back of a closet. 3. 12 4. from the Supply Depot, which gets supplies from Ember's storerooms 5. There is no natural light, so Ember depends on electricity for light. 6. He throws the paper with his job assignment on the floor and yells that Ember is not prospering. 7. There are no phones or computers in Ember, so messages sent through messengers are the only way for citizens to communicate with each other. 8. Light bulbs provide the only source of light in Ember. If Ember's bulb supply is exhausted, the citizens of Ember will be forced to live in the dark. 9. Supplies are dwindling. The citizens are very thrifty and do not waste anything. Luxuries are nonexistent. 10. Lina's ancestor, Podd Morethwart

Chapters 3–4: 1. He has never seen a river before. 2. Doon will not be allowed to work on the generator. Workers must have special permission to work on the generator because it is so crucial to Ember's survival. 3. about 50 feet underground 4. The Pipeworks is in poor condition, just like the rest of Ember. 5. because he has a mechanical mind and excels at taking things apart and putting them back together 6. to pay close attention to things and notice what no one else notices 7. Sadge Merrall, a man who recently ventured into the Unknown Regions but has since returned 8. The citizens are encouraged to not disagree or express concern at the mayor's decisions.

Chapters 5–6: 1. Lina usually eats potatoes with mushroom gravy and drinks beet tea for breakfast; because there are not many food choices. 2. Since Lina has the only steady job in the family, she most likely provides most of the family's income. However, Granny does own a yarn shop, which probably contributes a small portion. 3. Looper owns a store and sells Lina colored pencils. He sends a message to the mayor about a delivery on Lina's first day of work as a messenger. 4. Lina is frantic and guilt-ridden when she loses Poppy during the blackout. 5. seven minutes; The citizens know the exact length of the blackout because it is the longest Ember has ever experienced. 6. to reassure the citizens after the blackout 7. digging through a pile of things that she has removed from a closet

Chapters 7–8: 1. Its printing is unlike any she has ever seen. 2. Lina thinks Captain Fleery will know about official documents since she is the messenger captain. 3. Captain Fleery thinks that the message is a recipe or someone's school homework. 4. Nothing else exists beyond Ember. They are the only civilization, and Ember is "'the only light in the dark world'" (p. 25). 5. Most of the current storerooms are empty or sparsely filled. When Granny was young, the storerooms were fully stocked with a wide variety of food, school supplies, kitchenware, and tools. 6. Mayor Cole 7. his seriousness, curiosity, and detail-oriented nature 8. Answers will vary but should include three of the following: two new types of insects, a snail, a supply closet, a locked door, and a hatch. 9. alphabetically by topic

Chapters 9–10: 1. Mrs. Murdo is Lina's next-door neighbor who helps take care of Granny and Poppy while Lina is at work. 2. Doon likes to draw insects, and Lina likes to draw cities. 3. a lock 4. Lina traded her laborer job with Doon because she did not want to be in the damp, dark Pipeworks. 5. Lina and Doon see an unidentified man use a key to enter and exit the secret room. 6. She is low on medicine. 7. She doesn't know exactly what she's looking for—only that it's important. One can assume that Granny is worried about finding the box with the Instructions that once belonged to her grandfather, Podd Morethwart. 8. There is no sun or moon in Ember, nor do citizens have any electrical or illuminated clocks to tell time once the lights go out each night.

Chapters 11–12: 1. The Singing is an annual holiday when everyone in Ember gathers to sing the three great songs of Ember: "The Song of the River," "The Song of the City," and "The Song of Darkness." 2. with Mrs. Murdo 3. Lina realizes that she is now Poppy's mother figure, and it is up to her to take care of Poppy. Further, while she and Poppy live with Mrs. Murdo, Lina has no more living relatives to depend on. She matures because she realizes that Poppy is her only living relative. 4. because she has her arms full of canned goods that Looper has stolen from the storerooms 5. Looper 6. because they are afraid of being caught away from home during a blackout 7. a secret room where the mayor stores his stolen food and supplies 8. Looper 9. Lina and Doon tell Barton Snode and the guards at Gathering Hall.

Chapters 13–14: 1. Clary 2. He has made poor, foolish decisions about how to run Ember. He is wicked because he steals goods from the public storerooms for his own personal use. 3. the sprout that Clary gave Lina 4. Clary; "Instruction for Egress," which means instructions for exit 5. Doon goes into the Pipeworks office and takes the spare key when no one is looking. 6. The ladder cannot be seen from the pathway. 7. It slides from left to right instead of opening like a regular door. 8. Doon and Lina use candles and matches to create movable light, which allows them to see in the tunnel. 9. Boats are unnecessary in Ember because there are no bodies of water in the city.

Chapters 15–16: 1. The first boat is like a model to show Lina and Doon what a boat and paddles are and how they work. 2. so he can look at them later 3. Answers will vary but should include three of the following: rope, water bottle, folding knife, clothes, paper and pencil, food. 4. She tells the guards that she saw Doon going toward the trash heaps, when she has really seen no such thing. 5. Poppy's, Mrs. Murdo's, and Clary's safety and possibly having her family split apart in the rush to leave Ember 6. Clary 7. The people of Ember sing the three songs of Ember: "The Song of the River," "The Song of the City," and "The Song of Darkness." 8. Lina escapes during a blackout. 9. the flicker of the candle Doon took from the Pipeworks

Chapters 17–18: 1. a note that vaguely explains his and Lina's discovery 2. movable light 3. Poppy 4. Answers will vary. Suggestions: not knowing or being able to see where they are going, dropping or losing Poppy, having no control over their destination 5. because the river flows away from Ember, not toward it; They cannot guide their boat back upstream. 6. a diary 7. Lina forgets to deliver the note to Clary.

Chapters 19–20: 1. deep underground at the bottom of a cave or chasm 2. Answers will vary. Suggestions: the moon, the sun, grass, stars, birds, trees, insects, flowers, an animal (most likely a fox) 3. an older woman who was one of Ember's first inhabitants 4. Lina and Doon most likely see a fox in the meadow; No, the only animals in Ember appear to be insects. 5. the lights of Ember 6. Mrs. Murdo

Activity #13: Answers will vary. Suggestion: Doon Harrow; Doon helps Lina discover the escape route from Ember; He wants to fix Ember's problems but also wants recognition for himself; There is nothing significant about Doon's name; Doon is an important character who actively moves the plot along; Doon lives in Ember, when the city is in distress and needs repair; Doon's determination and methodical, calculating ways are important because they allow him and Lina to discover the way out of Ember; Doon becomes more self-confident throughout the story. He also grows more attached to Lina; Answers will vary; Answers will vary.

Activity #14: Answers will vary. Suggestions: Lina—social, a messenger, parents are both dead, main provider for her family, likes to run and talk to people; Doon—solitary, works in the Pipeworks, lives with his father, does not have to provide for his family, doesn't like to talk much but is very intense and contemplative; Doon and Lina—determined, work together to find the escape route, genuinely care about each other, generally kind-hearted, are risk-takers

Activity #15: Answers will vary. Suggestions: Characters—Doon Harrow and Lina Mayfleet; Time and Place—the city of Ember 241 years after it was built; Problem—Ember's generator is failing and supplies are running out; Goal—to find an escape route from Ember; Beginning/Development/Outcome—Poppy finds the Instructions. Lina and Doon decode the Instructions. Lina and Doon follow the Instructions and escape from Ember; Resolution—Lina and Doon arrive at the earth's surface and realize that Ember is underground. They toss a note down below to Ember to tell the citizens about the escape route.

Activity #16: Answers will vary.

Quiz #1: A. 1. T 2. T 3. F 4. T 5. F 6. F 7. T 8. T 9. F 10. F **B.** 11. h 12. e 13. a 14. j 15. i 16. b 17. c 18. g 19. d 20. f

Quiz #2: A. 1. a 2. f 3. c 4. d 5. e 6. b 7. a 8. g 9. d 10. h **B.** 11. F 12. T 13. F 14. T 15. T 16. F 17. F 18. T 19. F 20. F

Quiz #3: A. 1. c 2. g 3. i 4. d 5. e 6. j 7. b 8. h 9. a 10. f **B.** Graphic organizers will vary depending on which theme the student chooses. Suggestion: Theme—following one's dreams; Spokes—Doon and Lina trade to get the job assignments they want; Doon investigates the Pipeworks; Lina repeatedly dreams about a city of light; Lina perseveres to decode the Instructions; Lina and Doon search the Pipeworks several times to find an escape route; Lina escapes the mayor so she can leave Ember; Lina chooses to take Poppy with her; Lina and Doon navigate the river even though they are frightened of what awaits them.

Novel Test: A. 1. light 2. dark 3. 241 4. Assignment Day 5. Lina 6. messenger 7. Pipeworks 8. Harrow 9. generator 10. blackouts 11. grandmother 12. Poppy 13. Instructions 14. Looper 15. boyfriend 16. Mayor Cole 17. Singing 18. rock 19. E 20. candles/matches 21. matches/candles 22. boat 23. river 24. Unknown Regions 25. Poppy 26. journal/diary 27. sunrise 28. chasm/cave 29. note/message 30. Mrs. Murdo **B.** 31. d 32. a 33. b 34. c 35. d 36. b 37. a 38. d 39. b 40. c 41. c 42. b 43. b 44. c 45. d **C.** Essays will vary. Please refer to the scoring rubric on page 35 of this guide.

Linking Novel Units® Student Packets to National and State Reading Assessments

During the past several years, an increasing number of students have faced some form of state-mandated competency testing in reading. Many states now administer state-developed assessments to measure the skills and knowledge emphasized in their particular reading curriculum. This Novel Units® guide includes open-ended comprehension questions that correlate with state-mandated reading assessments. The rubric below provides important information for evaluating responses to open-ended comprehension questions. Teachers may also use scoring rubrics provided for their own state's competency test.

Scoring Rubric for Open-Ended Items

3-Exemplary
- Thorough, complete ideas/information
- Clear organization throughout
- Logical reasoning/conclusions
- Thorough understanding of reading task
- Accurate, complete response

2-Sufficient
- Many relevant ideas/pieces of information
- Clear organization throughout most of response
- Minor problems in logical reasoning/conclusions
- General understanding of reading task
- Generally accurate and complete response

1-Partially Sufficient
- Minimally relevant ideas/information
- Obvious gaps in organization
- Obvious problems in logical reasoning/conclusions
- Minimal understanding of reading task
- Inaccuracies/incomplete response

0-Insufficient
- Irrelevant ideas/information
- No coherent organization
- Major problems in logical reasoning/conclusions
- Little or no understanding of reading task
- Generally inaccurate/incomplete response

Notes